PEARL S. BUCK: THE COMPLETE WOMAN

Selections from the Writings of

Pearl S. Buck

Winner of the Nobel Prize for Literature

Edited by C. Merton Babcock

Professor of American Thought and Language

Michigan State University

Illustrated by Arlene Noel

Hallmark Editions

Pearl S. Buck:
The Complete Woman

Pearl Sydenstricker Buck was born in Hillsboro, West Virginia, on June 26, 1892. Taken to the interior of China at the age of three months by her missionary parents, Absolom and Caroline Sydenstricker, she virtually grew up in two separate worlds at once—"the small white clean Presbyterian American world" of the mission compound, and the "merry, not-too-clean Chinese world" in which she made her first friends and in which her life-style was determined by Oriental patterns. Although her earliest memories are of China, she was nevertheless an alien in that country as well as a total stranger to the land of her birth. "I'm not quite at home anywhere," she later confided, "and somewhat at home everywhere."

Pearl Sydenstricker's gifted mother educated her daughter in the ways of the Western world, and, among other things, taught her something of the beauty of language and the magic in verbal expression. At the age of 15, the young lady was placed in a boarding school in Shanghai, and, at 17, she accompanied her parents to Europe and England, and then to America, where she attended Randolph-Macon College and won two literary prizes during her senior year.

After graduation, the budding novelist returned to China, married John Lossing Buck, an American agriculturist, lived in North China for five years, and became the mother of two daughters. In 1921, her husband took a position in the University of Nanking, and she joined the staff as an English teacher.

Pearl Buck published her novel, EAST WIND, WEST WIND, in 1930, and, during the following year, her prize winning masterpiece, THE GOOD EARTH, for which she was awarded both the Pulitzer Prize and the William Dean Howells medal. Five years later, she was elected to membership in the National Institute of Arts and Letters, and, in 1938, she was awarded the Nobel Prize for Literature—a distinction shared by no other American woman.

Having divorced her husband in 1935, Mrs. Buck took up permanent residence in America. She married her publisher, Richard J. Walsh, and with her two daughters and four adopted children, they established a country home at Perkasie, Pennsylvania. During the four decades since she began publishing, the internationally famous novelist has turned out no fewer than eighty volumes of fiction, biography, works of general interest, children's stories and personal reminiscences.

At 78, Pearl Buck, essentially a writer, is also a defender of human rights and an advocate of international cooperation. She radiates good will, sympathy, love, all things that make her a perfect example of the complete woman.

Pearl S. Buck:

THE COMPLETE WOMAN

From THE GOOD EARTH

In this tender novel, Pearl Buck paints a striking word-portrait of her beloved China. THE GOOD EARTH *tells of Wang Lung, a Chinese landowner, and his wife O-lan, a former servant girl. Weaving their story into the varied fabric of Chinese life and custom, Mrs. Buck takes Wang Lung and O-lan through the first days of love and marriage; through the birth of their children; through their acquisition of wealth; through the difficult days when Wang Lung takes another woman into the house.* THE GOOD EARTH *is a*

7

*touching book. It is rich with Pearl Buck's awareness
of the beauty of life, the importance of work, and
the relationship between a woman and her man:*

There is not that about three rooms and two meals
a day to keep busy a woman who has been a slave
in a great house and who has worked from dawn
until midnight. One day when Wang Lung was hard
pressed with the swelling wheat and was cultivat-
ing it with his hoe, day after day, until his back
throbbed with weariness, her shadow fell across the
furrow over which he bent himself, and there she
stood, with a hoe across her shoulder.

"There is nothing in the house until nightfall," she
said briefly, and without speech she took the furrow
to the left of him and fell into steady hoeing.

The sun beat down upon them, for it was early
summer, and her face was soon dripping with her
sweat. Wang Lung had his coat off and his back bare,
but she worked with her thin garment covering her
shoulders and it grew wet and clung to her like skin.
Moving together in a perfect rhythm, without a
word, hour after hour, he fell into a union with her
which took the pain from his labor. He had no ar-
ticulate thought of anything; there was only this perfect sympathy of movement, of turning this earth
of theirs over and over to the sun, this earth which
formed their home and fed their bodies and made

their gods. The earth lay rich and dark, and fell apart lightly under the points of their hoes. Sometimes they turned up a bit of brick, a splinter of wood. It was nothing. Some time, in some age, bodies of men and women had been buried there, houses had stood there, had fallen, and gone back into the earth. So would also their house, some time, return into the earth, their bodies also. Each had his turn at this earth. They worked on, moving together—together —producing the fruit of this earth—speechless. . . .

When the sun had set he straightened his back slowly and looked at the woman. Her face was wet and streaked with the earth. She was as brown as the very soil itself. Her wet, dark garments clung to her square body. She smoothed a last furrow slowly. Then in her usual plain way she said, straight out, her voice flat and more than usually plain in the silent evening air, "I am with child."

Wang Lung stood still. What was there to say to this thing, then! She stooped to pick up a bit of broken brick and threw it out of the furrow. It was as though she had said, "I have brought you tea," or as though she had said, "We can eat." It seemed as ordinary as that to her! But to him—he could not say what it was to him. His heart swelled and stopped as though it met sudden confines. Well, it was their turn at this earth!

He took the hoe suddenly from her hand and he

said, his voice thick in his throat, "Let be for now. It is a day's end. We will tell the old man."

They walked home then, she half a dozen paces behind him as befitted a woman. The old man stood at the door, hungry for his evening's food, which, now that the woman was in the house, he would never prepare for himself. He was impatient and he called out, "I am too old to wait for my food like this!"

But Wang Lung, passing him into the room, said, "She is with child already."

He tried to say it easily as one might say, "I have planted the seeds in the western field today," but he could not. Although he spoke in a low voice it was to him as though he had shouted the words out louder than he would.

The old man blinked for a moment and then comprehended, and cackled with laughter.

"Heh-heh-heh—" he called out to his daughter-in-law as she came, "so the harvest is in sight!"

Her face he could not see in the dusk, but she answered evenly, "I shall prepare food now."

"Yes—yes—food—" said the old man eagerly, following her into the kitchen like a child. Just as the thought of a grandson had made him forget his meal, so now the thought of food freshly before him made him forget the child.

But Wang Lung sat upon a bench by the table in

the darkness and put his head upon his folded arms. Out of this body of his, out of his own loins, life!

This piece of land which Wang Lung now owned was a thing which greatly changed his life. At first, after he had dug the silver from the wall and taken it to the great house, after the honor of speaking as an equal to the Old Lord's equal was past, he was visited with a depression of spirit which was almost regret. When he thought of the hole in the wall now empty that had been filled with silver he need not use, he wished that he had his silver back. After all, this land, it would take hours of labor again, and as O-lan said, it was far away, more than a *li*, which is a third of a mile. And again, the buying of it had not been quite so filled with glory as he had anticipated. He had gone too early to the great house and the Old Lord was still sleeping. True, it was noon, but when he said in a loud voice, "Tell his Old Honor I have important business—tell him money is concerned!" the gateman had answered positively.

"All the money in the world would not tempt me to wake the old tiger. He sleeps with his new concubine, Peach Blossom, whom he has had but three days. It is not worth my life to waken him." And then he added somewhat maliciously, pulling at the hairs on his mole, "And do not think that silver will waken him—he has had silver under his hand since he was born."

In the end, then, it had to be managed with the Old Lord's agent, an oily scoundrel whose hands were heavy with the money that stuck to them in passing. So it seemed sometimes to Wang Lung that after all the silver was more valuable than the land. One could see silver shining.

Well, but the land was his! He set out one grey day in the second month of the new year to look at it. None knew yet that it belonged to him and he walked out to see it alone, a long square of heavy black clay that lay stretched beside the moat encircling the wall of the town. He paced the land off carefully, three hundred paces lengthwise and a hundred and twenty across. Four stones still marked the corners of the boundaries, stones set with the great seal character of the House of Hwang. Well, he would have that changed. He would pull up the stones later and he would put his own name there— not yet, for he was not ready for people to know that he was rich enough to buy land from the great house, but later, when he was more rich, so that it did not matter what he did. And looking at that long square of land he thought to himself, "To those at the great house it means nothing, this handful of earth, but to me it means how much!"

Then he had a turn of his mind and he was filled with a contempt for himself that a small piece of land should seem so important. Why, when he had poured out his silver proudly before the agent, the man had scraped it up carelessly in his hands and said, "Here is enough for a few days of opium for the old lady, at any rate."

And the wide difference that still lay between him and the great house seemed suddenly impassable as the moat full of water in front of him, and as high as the wall beyond, stretching up straight and hoary before him. He was filled with an angry determination, then, and he said to his heart that he would fill that hole with silver again and again until he had bought from the House of Hwang enough land so that this land would be less than an inch in his sight.

And so this parcel of land became to Wang Lung a sign and a symbol.

It was not to be supposed that the coming of this one called Lotus and of her serving woman Cuckoo into Wang Lung's house could be accomplished altogether without stir and discord of some sort, since more than one woman under one roof is not for peace. But Wang Lung had not foreseen it. And even though he saw by O-lan's sullen looks and Cuckoo's sharpness that something was amiss, he would not pay heed to it and he was careless of anyone so long as he was still fierce with his desire.

Nevertheless, when day passed into night, and night changed into dawn, Wang Lung saw that it was true the sun rose in the morning, and this woman Lotus was there, and the moon rose in its season and she was there for his hand to grasp when it would, and his thirst of love was somewhat slaked and he saw things he had not seen before.

For one thing, he saw that there was trouble at once between O-lan and Cuckoo. This was an astonishment to him, for he was prepared for O-lan to hate Lotus, having heard many times of such things, and some women will even hang themselves upon a beam with a rope when a man takes a second woman into the house, and others will scold and contrive to make his life worthless for what he has done, and he was glad that O-lan was a silent woman for at least she could not think of words against him. But he had not foreseen that whereas she would be silent of

Lotus, her anger would find its vent against Cuckoo.

Now Wang Lung had thought only of Lotus and when she begged him.

"Let me have this woman for my servant, seeing that I am altogether alone in the world, for my father and my mother died when I could not yet talk and my uncle sold me as soon as I was pretty to a life such as I have had, and I have no one."

This she said with her tears, always abundant and ready and glittering in the corners of her pretty eyes, and Wang Lung could have denied her nothing she asked when she looked up at him so. Besides, it was true enough that the girl had no one to serve her, and it was true she would be alone in his house, for it was plain enough and to be expected that O-lan would not serve the second one, and she would not speak to her or notice that she was in the house at all. There was only the wife of his uncle then, and it was against Wang Lung's stomach to have that one peeping and prying and near to Lotus for her to talk to him, and so Cuckoo was as good as any and he knew no other woman who would come.

But it seemed that O-lan, when she saw Cuckoo, grew angry with a deep and sullen anger that Wang Lung had never seen and did not know was in her. Cuckoo was willing enough to be friends, since she had her pay from Wang Lung, albeit she did not forget that in the great house she had been in the lord's chamber and O-lan a kitchen slave and one of many. Nevertheless, she called out to O-lan well enough when first she saw her, "Well, and my old friend, here we are in a house together again, and you mistress and first wife—my mother—and how things are changed!"

But O-lan only stared at her and when it came into her understanding who it was and what she was, she answered nothing but she put down the jar of water she carried and she went into the middle room where Wang Lung sat between his times of love, and she said to him plainly, "What is this slave woman doing in our house?"

Wang Lung looked east and west. He would have liked to speak out and to say in a surly voice of master, "It is my house and whoever I say may come in, she shall come in, and who are you to ask?" But he could not because of some shame in him when O-lan was there before him, and his shame made him angry, because when he reasoned it, there was no need for shame and he had done no more than any man may do who has silver to spare.

Still, he could not speak out, and he only looked east and west and feigned to have mislaid his pipe in his garments, and he fumbled in his girdle. But O-lan stood there solidly on her big feet and waited, and when he said nothing she asked again plainly in the same words, "What is this slave woman doing in our house?"

Then Wang Lung, seeing she would have an answer, said feebly, "And what is it to you?"

And O-lan said, "I bore her haughty looks all during my youth in the great house and her running into the kitchen a score of times a day and crying out 'now tea for the lord'—'now food for the lord'— and it was always this is too hot and that is too cold, and that is badly cooked, and I was too ugly and too slow and too this and too that. . . ."

But still Wang Lung did not answer, for he did not know what to say.

Then O-lan waited and when he did not speak, the hot, scanty tears welled slowly into her eyes, and she winked them to hold back the tears, and at last she took the corner of her blue apron and wiped her eyes and she said at last, "It is a bitter thing in my own house, and I have no mother's house to go back to anywhere."

And when Wang Lung was still silent and answered nothing at all, but he sat down to his pipe and lit it, and he said nothing still, she looked at him piteously and sadly out of her strange dumb eyes that were like a beast's eyes that cannot speak, and then she went away, creeping and feeling for the door because of her tears that blinded her.

Wang Lung watched her as she went and he was glad to be alone, but still he was ashamed and he was still angry that he was ashamed and he said to himself and he muttered the words aloud and restlessly, as though he quarreled with someone, "Well, and other men are so and I have been good enough to her, and there are men worse than I." And he said at last that O-lan must bear it.

As for Wang Lung, he said to himself that at last his affairs were settled and his women at peace and he could enjoy his love. And it seemed to him freshly that he could never tire of Lotus and of the way she pouted at him with the lids drooped like lily petals over her great eyes, and at the way laughter gleamed out of her eyes when she glanced up at him. One day he heard a shriek from the inner courts and he ran in for he heard it was the voice of Lotus, and there he found that the two younger children, the boy and the girl born alike, had between them led into the inner court his elder daughter, his poor fool. Now the four other children were constantly curious about this lady who lived in the inner court, but the two elder boys were conscious and shy and knew well enough why she was there and what their father had to do with her, although they never spoke of her unless to each other secretly. But the two younger ones could never be satisfied with their peepings and their exclamations, and sniffing of the perfume she wore and dipping their fingers into the bowls of food that Cuckoo carried away from her room after she had eaten.

Lotus complained many times to Wang Lung that his children were a plague to her and she wished there were a way to lock them out so that she need not be plagued with them. But this he was not willing to do, and he answered her in jest, "Well, and they like to look at a lovely face as much as their father does."

And he did nothing except to forbid them to enter her courts and when he saw them they did not, but when he did not see them they ran in and out secretly. But the elder daughter knew nothing of anything, but only sat in the sun against the wall of the outer court, smiling and playing with her bit of twisted cloth.

On this day, however, the two elder sons being away at school, the two younger children had conceived the notion that the fool must also see the lady in the inner courts, and they had taken her hands and dragged her into the court and she stood before

Lotus, who had never seen her and sat and stared at her. Now when the fool saw the bright silk of the coat Lotus wore and the shining jade in her ears, she was moved by some strange joy at the sight and she put out her hands to grasp the bright colors and she laughed aloud, a laugh that was only sound and meaningless. And Lotus was frightened and screamed out, so that Wang Lung came running in, and Lotus shook with her anger and leaped up and down on her little feet and shook her finger at the poor laughing girl and cried out, "I will not stay in this house if that one comes near me, and I was not told that I should have accursed idiots to endure and if I had known it I would not have come—filthy children of yours!" and she pushed the little gaping boy who stood nearest her, clasping his twin sister's hand.

Then the good anger awoke in Wang Lung, for he loved his children, and he said roughly, "I will not hear my children cursed, no and not by anyone and not even my poor fool, and not by you who have no son in your womb for any man." And he gathered the children together and said to them, "Now go out, my son and my daughter, and come no more to this woman's court, for she does not love you and if she does not love you she does not love your father, either." And to the elder girl he said with great gentleness, "And you, my poor fool, come back to

20

your place in the sun." And she smiled and he took her by the hand and led her away.

For he was most angry of all that Lotus dared to curse this child of his and call her idiot, and a load of fresh pain for the girl fell upon his heart, so that for a day and two days he would not go near Lotus, but he played with the children and he went into the town and he bought a circle of barley candy for his poor fool and he comforted himself with her baby pleasure in the sweet sticky stuff.

And when he went in to Lotus again neither of them said anything that he had not come for two days, but she took special trouble to please him, for when he came his uncle's wife was there drinking tea, and Lotus excused herself and said, "Now here is my lord come for me and I must be obedient to him for this is my pleasure," and she stood until the woman went away.

Then she went up to Wang Lung and took his hand and drew it to her face and she wooed him. But he, although he loved her again, loved her not so wholly as before, and never again so wholly as he had loved her.

There came a day when summer was ended and the sky in the early morning was clear and cold and blue as sea water and a clean autumn wind blew hard over the land, and Wang Lung woke as from a sleep. He went to the door of his house and he looked over his fields. And he saw that the waters had receded and the land lay shining under the dry cold wind and under the ardent sun.

Then a voice cried out in him, a voice deeper than love cried out in him for his land. And he heard it above every other voice in his life and he tore off the long robe he wore and he stripped off his velvet shoes and his white stockings and he rolled his trousers to his knees and he stood forth robust and eager and he shouted, "Where is the hoe and where the plow? And where is the seed for the wheat planting? Come, Ching, my friend—come—call the men —I go out to the land!"

ACCEPTANCE OF THE NOBEL PRIZE

In 1938 Pearl Buck received the Nobel Prize for Literature—the first American of her sex to be so honored. In her acceptance speech she acknowledged the occasion as a milestone for American womanhood:

YOUR ROYAL HIGHNESS:

LADIES AND GENTLEMEN:

It is not possible for me to express all that I feel of appreciation for what has been said and given to me. I accept, for myself, with the conviction of having received far beyond what I have been able to return through my books. I can only hope that the many books which I have yet to write will be in some measure a worthier acknowledgment than I can make tonight. And indeed, I can accept only in the same spirit in which I think this gift was originally given—that is, a prize not so much for what has been done as for the future. Whatever I write in the future must, I think, be always benefited and strengthened when I remember this day.

I accept, too, for my country, the United States of America. We are a people still young and we know that we have not yet come to the fullness of our powers. This award, given to an American, strengthens not only one, but the whole body of American writers, who are encouraged and heartened by such generous recognition. And I should like to say, too, that in my country it is important that this award has been given to a woman. You who have already so recognized your own Selma Lagerlöf, and have long recognized women in other fields, cannot perhaps wholly understand what it means in many countries and even in my own, that it is a woman who stands here at this moment. But I speak not only for writers and for women, but for all Americans, for we all share in this occasion.

I should not be truly myself if I did not, in my own wholly unofficial way, speak also of the people of China, whose life has for so many years been my life also, whose life, indeed, must always be a part of my life. The minds of my own country and of China, my foster country, are alike in many ways, but above all, alike in our common love of freedom. . . . Freedom—it is today more than ever the most precious human possession. We—Sweden and the United States—we have it still. My country is young —but it greets you with a peculiar fellowship, you whose earth is ancient and free.

WHAT SHALL I TELL MY DAUGHTER?

What does a mother tell a daughter who is about to be married? Pearl Buck answers this question eloquently in the following selection from her book TO MY DAUGHTERS WITH LOVE:

She is to be married. I see that at once as she comes to my door. I am as usual at my desk, but this room, dedicated to my work and my art, is always open to my child. She is, of course, no longer a child. She is twenty years old, and I have known for the last two years that some morning she would stand at my door, looking at me shyly with that peculiar radiance which love and only love gives to a woman. She can never achieve it alone, however sacred the cause to which she dedicates herself. It is only when she knows the man whom she loves loves her that her eyes glow with the mysterious light, her skin takes on translucence, her cheeks flush, her lips part in half-smiling joy at once innocent and profound.

"Come in, my darling," I say.

"Are you busy?" she inquires, not so much in concern for my work as in hesitation. How can she convey to me the extraordinary news? Will I understand that a young man who was only recently a little boy with grubby hands and mischievous face, a gangling youth whose hair was unbrushed and too long, a callow young man who went off to college. . . .

"I have something to tell you," she informs me.

She comes in, sits down in the worn armchair and spreads her pink skirts. She looks very pretty this morning, quite apart from love. Her dark hair is shining with health and good grooming, her skin is tanned by the summer sun, and her lips are red with natural health.

"You look very nice today—even nicer than usual," I say by way of encouragement.

She does not appear to hear my remark. Ah well, she is accustomed to being told that she is beautiful. Her violet eyes, set in long, black lashes under fine, dark brows, are grave with purpose.

"Mother?"

"Yes, my child?"

"I suppose you have noticed that he and I—"

I cannot resist a teasing impulse. "He? Darling, which 'he' do you mean?"

Young men surround her and there are at least four whom I imagine as quite possible in varying ways—four, that is, whom I would find acceptable as. . . .

"Mother!" she exclaims in horror. "As if it could be anyone but Peter!"

Peter? But I have not thought of Peter. I thought of course it would be—and why Peter? She has only known him for six months. He is seven years older than she is. That is to say, twenty-seven is much older than twenty. At twenty-seven a man has already been in love several times, in all probability, and she has never been in love before—not like this!

"Peter?" I cannot hide my surprise.

"But you said you liked him!" Her eyes, very blue and accusing, open wide and fill with unexpected tears.

I leave my seat at once and run to her side.

"Darling, of course I like him. I just don't think you know him well enough for—"

"I knew the moment I saw him. And he knew. He proposed to me within the week."

"You didn't—"

"Oh no, I didn't accept him at once. I remembered what you said about that—you said you married too quickly the first time and that was why there had to be a second time, when you were really in love. I waited for six months to pass."

"Six months?" I repeat stupidly. I sit down on the big hassock at her feet.

She is impatient with me. "You said—don't you remember?—a girl should know a man for six months at least. Well, it was six months last night, at quarter past eight, and he stood beside me under the sycamore tree at the end of the lane, his watch in his hand until the minute came up—"

We both laugh. She leans forward to give me a quick embrace and releases me as quickly.

"Of course," she goes on, smoothing her skirt, "they were unnecessary, those six months."

"I am not so sure," I retort. "You may be glad for them later."

She pays no heed to this. It is obvious that she hears nothing I say. She pushes back her dark hair.

"We don't want a long engagement," she announces.

"Which is to tell me that you want to be married as soon as possible," I retort.

"Next month, on the fifteenth, at four o'clock. It's a special date, a special hour."

I do not allow myself to ask questions. Her memories are already sacred to herself and to him. She is not looking at me. She is looking at her hands, folded on her lap. One hand is over the other.

"Let me see your ring," I say.

She holds up her left hand. A single diamond, not too large, for she is petite, this child of mine, but a fine, clear diamond, not too small either, and beautifully set, shines on her third finger.

"He had it all ready for me," she tells me softly.

"He was sure of you, then?"

"Of course," she says with calm.

I marvel at the honesty of my child. In this she is a true daughter of her times. The old fencing between man and woman, the ancient coquetries, are cast aside, it seems. She is not in the least ashamed of her readiness to love this man Peter.

We sit in silence for a moment, I still holding her left hand as I consider Peter. Will he be tender with her? Will he understand her need for solitude? Will he love her little willful ways? There is so much of the child in her still and always must be, I think. She has a native innocence, the sense of reality which children have—and very great people also.

She draws her hand away gently and covers it again with her right hand, as something too dear, too personal, too close, even for me to see or to hold.

The strange pause continues between us. She breaks it, and, to my surprise, with tears again in her eyes.

"Oh, Mother—" her voice chokes in a half sob.

"What is it, my darling? Why do you cry?"

"I don't know! Perhaps I'm afraid . . . a little—"

"Afraid? Not of him?"

"Of . . . of love . . . of not being able to make him happy. He is so intelligent . . . much more than I am. You know that. He is clever and . . . and educated . . . and . . . and. . . . "

This is true. Peter is an intellectual, a young scientist, an artist in his area. I know the type. My child is also well educated, but not in the same field. A mathematical equation means nothing to her while to Peter it is his language.

"Oh, Mother!" she wails. Her head is suddenly on my shoulder. I feel her soft hair on my cheek. "If he ever stops loving me . . . I'll die!"

I smooth back the hair and feel the flushed cheek. "Now, now," I say in my most practical voice, "how do you think he would feel if you stopped loving him? He'd want to die, too—perhaps."

I add the "perhaps" for caution and she comprehends.

She lifts her head and wipes the tears away with her small handkerchief, pulled from her belt.

"No, he wouldn't," she says flatly. "Men don't. They have so many things to think about. That's what I'm afraid of. He could stop loving me without realizing it . . . sort of . . . you know, the way men do."

"Women do, too, sometimes," I put in.

30

She shakes her head at this. Impossible, the violet eyes declare, incredible that she should ever stop loving Peter!

"Oh yes," I maintain. "If one stops loving, the other does, too. It's mutual, this falling in love—and out again."

"Oh no!" she cries with passion. "I don't want to stop loving him. What shall I do? I don't know about love . . . not really, not enough!"

I cannot answer her at once. What shall I tell my daughter about love? It takes thinking. There is so much to tell. I cannot overwhelm her with my own experience, I, who know the many ways in which a man can be loved—yes, and be taught to love—for I am not sure that men know by instinct, as women do, what love is. They are confused and complicated by the powerful drive of physical sex, so much more simple and single than the woman's sexual drive.

If she is not wary and wise and sensitive and, above all, if she does not love him enough, the relationship degenerates. The marriage becomes the humdrum of every day. The magic is gone.

Yet it is not true that this is inevitable—too usual, perhaps, but not inevitable. And it is the woman's— what is the right word?—not task, not duty, a little of these, but joy is the essence. It is the woman's joy to keep love at the level of delight and companionship and, yes, and of romance. It is a word misused and made contemptible by cheap people in cheap ways, but a word of rich emotion in spite of that.

"Leave me a little while, darling," I tell my child. "Go and find Peter. I'm sure he's waiting for you. When you are alone again, I'll be ready for you. I must sort things out in my own mind—what's important and what isn't."

She rises with such alacrity that I know Peter is waiting outside the door. I am right.

"Come in, Peter," she cries. "I've told her."

The door opens. I like what I see. He stands there, tall and slim and slightly embarrassed. He has brushed his fair hair with unusual care and he has forgotten his glasses. I see his dark eyes clearly. They are tender and humorous.

"Good morning," he says and stops. How does one go on from there? He makes a brave effort.

"I hope you are not shocked."

"Shocked?" I repeat the word and let it hang for an instant.

He tries to be nonchalant. He sits down. "Dare I hope you are pleased?"

"You may hope," I reply cruelly. "I shall find out after the years pass. This child is my treasure."

He puts aside all pretense. "I know," he says in a low voice. "And I am too old for her perhaps. Too much of an intellectual and all that? But she is my treasure, too. I cannot live without her. I have not thought of a woman since I first saw her walking down the street one day last spring. She passed me and I looked back at her and she looked back at me. It began in that moment. It will go on forever."

He is so earnest that I want to believe him.

"I hope so," I tell him. "And of course I am pleased that she is happy. Now leave me, my children. I have work to do."

They leave me, hand in hand and forgetting to close the door. I close it, but I do not return to my desk. I sit down in the worn armchair. I lean back and close my eyes. My life comes flooding in upon the tides of memory. I have been in love—yes, more than once. I have loved men in different ways, for different reasons. I still love. One never grows too old. That is a discovery. Man or woman, we never grow too old for love. I say it is a discovery, for when young I supposed that love belonged only to youth. And yet, when I was halfway through my life, I fell in love again and it seemed to me that it was for the first time. Years passed, happy years, and when they were ended and I was left alone, I said to myself that now love was over. I had loved my heart out and I could not love again. Then I made the discovery. The heart does not die. It maintains its habits of love. Not the same, it is true, for the ways of the heart are manifold and of infinite variety.

Shall I tell my child this truth? No! She is too young to know. Let her believe what she must believe now—that this is her one and only love. There must be no shadow of the future. It will fall upon her at the destined hour, and life itself will have prepared her for change—life or death. I will speak to her of something more important than love. I will speak to her of herself.

I will say to her something like this:

"The question is not whether you ever stop loving him or he ever stops loving you. The question is, do you know who you are? Well, I will tell you. You are a woman. In many ways you are a fortunate woman. You have beauty, you have intelligence. But these are perquisites and not necessities. They are gifts for which you should be thankful, and which you should use to the utmost. But if you had not these gifts, you would still be a woman and you would still have the necessity to know what it means to be a woman.

"You ask what this means? It means that you are a creation entirely different from man. True, nature does not discriminate between male and female in the distribution of her gifts. A daughter may inherit the brains, and not the son. She may have much while he may have little. Yet the fact that you have intelligence does not mean that it is the same intelligence the man has. Your intelligence is expressed through your woman material, and it is not the same as the man material. It is as though clear spring water were poured into a rose-red glass bowl and appeared rose red. If the same spring water were poured into a blue-glass bowl it would appear blue. Essentially it is the same but the container changes the hue. You will have the same impulses that Peter has, certainly the same need for love, but it will be expressed differently.

"He will express his love with ardor and frequency

through physical sex, for example. To him it is the way he can best express his love. Warm words, kisses, embraces so precious to you, so needed, are needed by him, too, but as introduction to the final demand of his body. Ah yes, you will agree to this finale, you will respond, at times welcome it and at times even invite it, but it will be the last step, not always essential. For him it is first and all-important.

You are to remember, then, that you are woman. Your love permeates your whole being. You are fortunate in the many ways you have of expressing love. To arrange his house, to plan his meals, to care for his comfort, to serve him—yes, I insist upon the word, for such service is sacred to love, even in the simplest and most menial ways. Menial? Nothing is menial where there is love.

"I tell you frankly that you must teach him the many ways of expressing love. The whole joy of sex is not in a single act. It is a prevailing atmosphere, a pervading life between man and woman, uniting in love two separate and different beings. He is a direct and sometimes blundering creature, this man. If he does not please you, laugh at him a little, but tenderly, and lead him along pleasant paths to the full understanding of your woman nature. Do not expect him to learn without being taught. If you do not teach him, some other woman may—or may already have done so. Above all, do not blame him for ignorance about you. You see why you must not be ignorant about yourself. If you do not understand yourself as a woman, how can you teach him?

"And let him teach you about himself. Do not pretend to know everything. You are ignorant about him because you are not a man, just as he is ignorant about you because he is not a woman. Teach one another and rejoice in being so taught. The more each knows of the other, the happier both will be. And you will never know everything, either of you, for in this mutual teaching—from the smallest detail, as for example how he likes his coffee, to the deepest and most profound matter of private love— you will discover that you are both growing and developing and reaching new levels of emotion and intelligence. There is nothing so fertilizing to the growth of the individual man and woman as the love between them, a growing, living love, which is to say, true, love. He will never stop loving you if he finds something always new in you, and through you in himself. Nor will you ever stop loving him. Love dies only when growth stops.

What was it that a wise old Chinese said five

hundred years before our Christian era? A disciple asked him whether a certain way was the right way, and Lao-tze replied: "It is a way, but not the eternal way."

You may test the truth of your love by your own growth as a woman and his as a man. If you are both growing in happiness, improving in mind and body, then your way of loving is the eternal way.

Yet do not worry yourself or even inquire of yourself as to whether you are growing. You will know that you are growing, for love will keep you informed. You will be happy—yes, even though there may be occasional disagreement. I will not use the word quarrel, for only children quarrel, without regard to facts or truth. Never descend to such trifling behavior with him. It is not important to know *who* is right. It is only important to know *what* is right. And you will discover that truth together and only together. A one-sided conclusion, declared by one against the other will be only a half truth and worth nothing. The one who insists and prevails by insistence takes the first step toward the death of love. Do not compete with him, for competition is impossible between you. Neither can lose and neither wins. I deny the battle of the sexes. If we do battle, then the battle is already lost and for both. Victory is only to be achieved in unity—victory over life and, yes, over death.

"Accept your womanhood, my daughter, and rejoice in it. It is your glory that you are a woman, for this is why he loves you, he whom you love. Be gentle, be wise, as a woman is gentle and wise. Be ardent and love with a woman's ardor. Through your love, teach him what it means to be a man, a noble man, a strong man. Believe in him, for only through your belief can he believe in himself. In our secret hearts, man and woman, we long above all else to know that the other, the one we love, knows what we are and believes in what we can be. Is this not romance? Yes, and the highest romance, investing the smallest detail of life with the color of joy.

"You observe, my darling child, that I say nothing of the duties of housewifery or motherhood or care of your person or even of the preservation of your beauty and charm. All such duties are easy enough to perform if you have this knowledge of yourself as woman. For if you know yourself as woman, you will comprehend your own need of him, your primary and profound need. Without him, you are only half a woman, as without you he is less than a man. Stay together, you two—never let him go, and never leave him, once your love is established and alive. Stay together, cling hand in hand, walk step in step, sleep close, so that you know forever that you are not alone!"

FOR THE LOVE OF A MAN

The ancient Chinese considered small feet to be the mark of a beautiful woman. For centuries Chinese women have bound their feet, enduring pain and disfigurement in order to please their men. This selection from Mrs. Buck's novel EAST WIND, WEST WIND *describes the trauma of breaking with tradition—and the tenderness one modern woman receives from her understanding husband:*

When I look back now, I realize that my husband's interest began in me that evening. It seemed as though before this we had nothing to talk about. Our thoughts never met. I could only watch him wondering and not understanding, and he never looked at me at all. When we spoke it was with the courtesy of strangers to each other, I with shyness towards him, he with careful politeness that overlooked me. But now that I had need of him he saw me at last, and when he spoke he questioned me and cared to hear my answer. As for me, the love that had been trembling in my heart for him steadied into adoration then. I had never dreamed that a man could stoop so tenderly to a woman.

When I asked him how I could unbind my feet, I thought, of course, that he would merely give me directions from his medical knowledge. And so I sat astounded when he himself fetched a basin of hot water and a roll of white bandage. I was ashamed. I could not endure having him see my feet. No one had seen them since I was old enough to care for them myself. Now, when he set the basin on the floor and knelt to take my feet, my whole body burned.

"No," I said faintly. "I will do it myself."

"You must not mind," he answered. "I am a doctor, you remember."

Still I refused. Then he looked me steadfastly in the face.

"Kwei-lan," he said gravely, "I know it costs you something to do this for me. Let me help you all I can. I am your husband."

Without a word then, I yielded. He took my foot, and gently he withdrew the shoe and stocking and unwound the inner cloth. His expression was sad and stern.

"How you have suffered!" he said in a low, tender voice; "how wretched a childhood—and all for nothing!"

The tears came into my eyes at his words. He was making useless all the sacrifice, and even demanding a new sacrifice!

For when my feet had been soaked and bound again more loosely, intolerable suffering set it. Indeed, the unbinding process was almost as painful as the binding had been. My feet, accustomed to constriction, gradually stretched a little, and the blood began to circulate.

There were times in the day when I tore at the bandages to unfasten them and bind them more tightly to ease me; and then the thought of my husband and that he would know at night made me replace them with trembling hands. The only slight respite I could get was to sit on my feet and rock back and forth.

No longer did I care how I appeared before my husband, or look in the mirror to see if I were at least fresh and neat. At night my eyes were swollen with weeping, and my voice wrought with sobs I could not control. Strange that when my beauty could not move him, my distress did! He would comfort me as though I were a child. I clung to him often without realizing. . .who or what he was.

"We will endure this together, Kwei-lan," he said. "It is hard to see you suffer so. Try to think that it is not only for us but for others, too—a protest against an old and wicked thing."

"No!" I sobbed, "I do it only for you—to be a modern woman for you!"

He laughed and his face lighted a little, as it had when he talked to that other woman. This was my reward for pain. Nothing seemed quite so hard afterwards.

And indeed, as the flesh grew more healthy I began to know a new freedom. I was young, and my feet were yet sound. Often in older women bound feet will mortify and sometimes even drop away. But mine were only numbed. Now I began to walk more freely, and the stairs were not so difficult. I felt stronger all over my body. One evening I ran without thinking into the room where my husband was writing. He looked up in surprise, and his face broke into a smile.

"Running?" he exclaimed. "Ah, well, we are over the worst then, and the bitterness is eaten."

COURAGE

Courage is one trait of the complete woman. In this excerpt from her book TO MY DAUGHTERS WITH LOVE, *Pearl Buck gives her unique definition of courage. And she tells the story of her mother, a living example of that definition:*

Let me define it first by saying that it is not bravado. Bravado is the pretense of feeling what one does not feel, a show of being what one is not. Bravado may be useful sometimes, but not for long and not for any continuing effort. Bravado may give one the moment necessary for summoning the reserves of courage, but one cannot depend upon it. It always breaks.

Courage does not break. It is secret strength. It is reserve power. When I hear the word *courage*, when I speak it, when I write it down, I think of a scene that took place before I was born. I know it only because my mother told me of it. She told me in the simple, unpretentious way in which she spoke of herself. How many other events she never told which might have been equal examples of courage, I do not know. This one stays with me; I see it as though I were there. Here it is.

The place is a city deep in the interior of China, and the time many decades ago. I do not know the exact year, but my mother, now long dead, was then a young woman with two small children. She was alone in the city, the only white woman, the only white person, except the children, for my father was away on one of his long journeys. The season was late summer. It had been a dry, hot summer. No rain had fallen for many weeks. The rice crop in the fields outside the city wall had dried before harvest. The wells in the city were low. People were hungry and frightened. What would they have for winter food? Why had this catastrophe fallen upon them? The gods were angry, their priests told them. The gods were angry because strangers, white people, were in the city.

My mother, staying close within the wall of the compound where she lived, knew what the people were muttering outside in the streets. She was told by her faithful servants, especially by the amah who helped her care for the children. At their pleading she had given up walks and shopping.

"Stay inside the gate, mistress," they begged. "Let the people think you went away with the master."

She obeyed, but she knew that the people did not think she had gone away. Their anger focused upon her as the summer passed without rain and upon the house which she had made into a home for her little family in an alien land. Day by day she hoped for my father's return, but she did not know when that would be. Mails were uncertain, for letters were brought by foot carriers who delayed or did not arrive at all. She could only wait, hoping against hope for rain. And day after day the skies were the same blue, hard and clear. She felt the deepening dispair of the people, and with it their rising fury. Sooner or later the fury would break. Over the walls, she heard the noise of parades and processions as the people carried their gods from the temples to reproach them with the sight of the bleak fields, the roads and streets deep in dust, the dried wells.

To her own God, my mother prayed, too, for rain. With all her heart she prayed as she went about her household tasks and as she cared for her children. In the hot, sleepless nights she prayed. Still there was no rain, and she knew that sooner or later the climax would come. The people would attack her and the children. In their fury, they would destroy the strangers within their city as a propitiation to the gods. It was more than her own conviction; the servants were hourly more afraid. They were faithful but they hid themselves behind the barred gate. One of them crept out at night to buy food secretly for the next day. Day and night they kept themselves quiet, speaking in low tones, hushing the children when they cried. My mother did not even play the small organ she had brought from her home in her own country, though music was always her solace.

One day dawned even more sultry than the rest.

The sky was white-hot and not a breath stirred the dying leaves on the bamboos in the garden. She knew that this was the day, she told me years later. She could feel the menace that hung over the silence in the city. The streets were empty, and not even the children shouted in play.

Late that afternoon her amah came to her in terror. "Mistress," she whispered, "they are coming tonight to kill you and the children."

My mother told me that she received this news without thought of escape. She knew there was no escape. No one in the city would dare to help her or protect her. She must face whatever was to come.

At that moment, my mother said, peace came into her heart and mind. The day drew to its end and she understood what she must do. Quietly she fed the children. Then she bathed them and put on their best clothes. She dressed herself in her simple best and brushed her hair well. All this time the amah helped her but in complete amazement. What was this white woman about to do? Did she plan to kill herself and the children? Meantime the silence in the streets had broken. An ominous roar took its place. My mother knew that a mob was gathering and attack was imminent.

"Set out all our tea bowls and make fresh tea," she directed her cook. "Put the small cakes you made . . .on plates and any fruit that we have as well."

To the gardener she said, "Open the gates of the compound—open them wide!"

They were all amazed, she told me, but she insisted and they obeyed. Then she herself opened the doors of the house and she and the children sat in the main room, they with their toys and she with her sewing. They were not frightened, for she showed no fear.

The mob howled in the streets. They surged through the open gates, carrying sticks and knives. She put down her sewing, and when they crowded the door of the house, she said, "Come in, come in and drink tea. I have been expecting you. You are welcome."

The men stared at her calm, smiling face. They took in the scene, the children playing and unafraid, the lamplit room, the tea and food on the table. My mother was pouring tea as she urged them to come in. She prattled on, telling them that her husband was not at home, that she was alone here with her good servants and the children.

They came in, uncertain and dazed, and the children, accustomed to the usually kind Chinese, left their toys and came to them without fear. My mother gave them tea, careful to hold each bowl in both hands, in courtesy to guests.

"What happened then?" I always asked this question, breathless with suspense, though I knew the story well because I wanted often to hear it.

"They drank the tea and ate the cakes," she replied. "Not at once of course, but bit by bit. They watched the children. Then everybody went away."

"Why?"

"I don't know."

"Were you afraid?"

"I was sick with fear."

"Then how did you have such courage?"

"From despair."

That is what she always said. The courage came from despair.

"If I had not had my back to the wall, if I had not had to face the situation from which there was no escape, I could not have found the courage."

Best of all, the end of the story was happy. For in the night as she lay sleepless with exhaustion, the rain fell. Unbelievable, but true! She heard it on the roof of the house and it was pure music.

"And the next morning"—she always told me by way of finish—"the whole city slept. No business was done, shops were not open. Everyone slept all day—and so did I."

IN DEFENSE OF WOMEN

"Decide what you want to be and be it" is Pearl Buck's message to womankind. Mrs. Buck is not a women's-lib extremist. She doesn't believe in a masculine conspiracy. But she does believe that women have not sufficiently established their identity in their own minds. "To be worthy of man's love," she writes, "woman has to be true to her deepest principles." Here she tells how that can be accomplished:

Man and woman are very different beings. This difference penetrates to the last atom of body and brain cell. In their difference is the hope of the race. And since woman is traditionally and historically wiser than man and more closely linked to the realities of the human group, her first task will be to understand herself and the reasons for her present state of mind. She must then understand man and the reasons for his need to insist upon himself as the ruler. She will have to convince him that he need not so insist because he need not fear her. She does not intend to return to her former place of power. Neither, however, does she wish man to be the dictator. She must remember how very recently man has discovered his own importance in the life scheme.

Women in other civilizations and indeed, in our own until recent years, have been the force for realism. Less emotional than men, more individualistic than men, infinitely more practical than men in terms of human life, women have through the centuries held in their hands the spiritual reins of their peoples. Men have loved best and most faithfully those women who are most worthy of love and faith. And to be worthy of man's love, woman has to be true to her deepest principles. Whenever she has lost her power as woman it has been because she has forsaken her own soul and has yielded to the soul of man. It is equally true, too, that where man has lost his power as man it is because he has yielded his soul to woman. Neither is ruler of the other. The union of man and woman has been closest, most satisfactory, and most fruitful when it has been part of the fulfillment of life itself—that is, when it became union for common and enlarging progress. No one woman can provide continuing interest for a man merely as an individual, neither can one man provide continuing interest for a woman as an individual. It is when together they contribute to a growing common life, a life larger than either of them, or than both together, that the personal relationship deepens enough to make the hearts of the two forever one.

When women say, therefore, that their place today is in the home, it is a lonely place. The average American woman in the home of average income is far too much alone. It is, I think, a devastating loneliness. For she was once a part of her world, and if it was a world of wilderness, still, man and child were with her and together they made a comforting, companionable unit. But now she has not that companionship. She listens to as much as they will tell her, she reads as much as she is inclined, she potters about on the fringe of the world that really goes on without her, and comforts herself at least by having a good hot dinner ready at night. It is not enough. The feeling one has after coming to know American women is that they are starving at their sources. And the sources of woman are man and child, as she is a part of their sources. . . .

That early American home was the center of civilization, the only seat of learning, the one resource of the humanities, and to woman the man and child looked for spiritual comfort and counsel. But now civilization and learning and the humanities, as well as the livelihood, are found outside the home. And more serious to woman even than the removal of the need for her physical labor, is the fact that she is no longer the spiritual and moral influence she was once to man and child in the home. . . . If woman is to recapture the lost companionship with man and child, she must once more forget herself, as she did in the old pioneer days, and follow them into the world.

Today, women may choose their sphere, even though they be wives, for the modern trend is for husband and wife to accept equal responsibility in home life except perhaps for a few necessary years when the wife is bearing children. This is good, but not good enough, for women are still far from having an equal voice with men in the policy-making centers of community life, national and international, in spite of comparable education and skills. This right, women, of course, must and will assert for themselves, for it is the final and most important step in their progress toward a full companionship with men, based on mutual freedom and shared responsibility at home and in the world.

Women must help each other, first of all, by believing in themselves. Then they will believe in and help one another. Whenever, for example, I hear a woman say she trusts a doctor because he is a man rather than a woman, I know that here is a woman who has a low opinion of herself. Otherwise she would choose the best doctor she could find, man or woman. A woman, to put it bluntly, is against other women because she fears she herself is inferior. Yet if she stopped to reason, she would realize that nature knows no sex limitations and does not bestow brains upon men alone. Daughters inherit gifts exactly as often and as much as sons.

What is a wife's chief responsibility today?

It is to prove to her husband, and through him to all men, that he need never fear her as she moves toward that complete equality with him in life which alone can bring happiness for them both.

And what is the husband's responsibility?

It is to encourage and help his wife, and through her all women, to be her free self, and so to release her talents for the world as well as the home.

When these mutual responsibilities are fulfilled, American marriages will, I believe, be even more rewarding than they are now.

A few years ago I heard an American woman put into one trenchant sentence the whole problem. She said, "Why doesn't somebody tell us what we are supposed to be so we can be it?"

My answer to that question was, I now know, quite superficial. I said, "Why should you ask anyone what you are supposed to be? Why not decide what you want to be and be it?"

THE PURSUIT OF HAPPINESS

*Happiness may not be, as Hawthorne said, a butter-
fly that alights upon us if we will only wait. In Pearl
Buck's world, happiness must be achieved. "No one
has promised happiness to us," she writes. Here she
discusses her own plan for the pursuit of that elusive
"butterfly":*

First let me say that the most important lesson life
has taught me is that happiness, or even contentment,
has to be planned for and worked for if it is to be
achieved. No one on earth or in heaven has promised happiness or even contentment to any of us. We
are born without promises. We find ourselves here,
enclosed in a body which was not of our making and
which may be very different from the one we would
like to have had, and belonging to a group of per-
sons, called a family, which may or may not be to
our liking, either. Yet each of us has certain talents
and potentials for happiness and each of us is given
the instrument by which we may put them to use.
This instrument is the will. Some people use this instrument well and they find contentment and conse-
quent happiness of a very permanent sort. Others
never use the instrument, and their lives sink into an
habitual discontent that can only result in permanent
unhappiness.

What directs the will? It does not work alone. It is only an instrument. It is the mind that directs the will. The mind says, "This must be done if happiness is to follow." For the will is a laggard. It likes to sleep. It prefers not to exert itself unless compelled. The mind must compel. Mind says, "I know this is what I must do, because it is what I want to do for my own contentment." And mind summons the will and insists upon performance. Will is what makes you get up in the morning when mind says there is work to be done. It is so easy to change night into day by sitting up all hours doing nothing much. Then day changes into night and nothing at all gets done. Discontent and unhappiness follow, since it is essential for the human creature to do and to be. Mind, then, is the planner, and will is the performer.

And in what area will the mind plan for contentment and for happiness? Let me recommend, from my own experience, that it be in the area of the arts —in music, in painting, in writing, in sculpture, in dance—the range is infinite. You will ask, is this not simply saying that one must have a hobby? No, I do not mean a hobby. Ideally, one should decide what one likes best to do and then train the self to earn a living in that field. But this is not always possible. Sometimes talent is insufficient for earning a living, yet enough to provide for happiness. It is then worth the effort of pursuit. You will enjoy art more if you pursue it without thought of money. Pursue it for pleasure, for release, for enrichment of the mind and spirit, for simple happiness. You will find that contentment follows. The tasks of daily life, then, are not so dreary, sorrow is lightened, loneliness becomes endurable.

Of course you must work. The will of the artist is his means of achievement, his energy. He soon learns that if he does not work, if he fills his time idly, he will be discontented and unhappy. . . .

Even after many years I can still think of a dozen ways not to sit down to my typewriter in the morning. The will needs a whip sometimes to get it started, and the mind must provide the whip. "No," mind must insist, "the flowers cannot be watered now or the newspaper read or that telephone call made, or anything else done except work."

When the will cannot escape, it performs, and when it performs, mind has to work, too. It is a curious interrelationship, this between mind and will. Mind decides for the will, and will gets to work upon mind. Long ago I learned that writing, for example, cannot depend upon the mood of the mind. Will sets mood aside and works upon mind, and mind, often reluctant at first, learns the habit of work. If mood is the ruler, then both will and mind fall into habits of lazy decay.

I know how difficult it is to understand the relationship of mind and will, especially at the beginning of learning an art. There is a certain amount of drudgery in every art. One cannot, for example, play the simplest piece of music without practice. But what joy when even the simple piece is mastered and can really be played! I recommend music, hopefully begun with a teacher, for art is most enjoyable when it is based upon accurate knowledge, even though performance never goes beyond the primary stage.

There is also sculpture, a supremely satisfying form of art, employing hands as well as mind and spirit. When my children were small and my life was overcrowded with daily duties, I found rest and release in modeling their heads in clay or plaster. I caught them on the wing as they played, and though the heads were far from perfect from a professional point of view, they were likenesses. I look at them with tender memory now that the children are grown men and women.

But why should I enumerate the arts? Art is various and always new.

What I am saying, in brief, is that the pursuit of art through some chosen form, planned for and achieved by determination and persistence, brings permanent contentment and the illumination of genuine happiness to the human spirit. Life is never dull, the creature is never bored, when he—or she—becomes the creator.

IMPORTANT DATES
IN PEARL S. BUCK'S LIFE

1892	Born June 26, in Hillsboro, West Virginia. Spent childhood in China, mostly at Chinkiang.
1910	Travelled in Europe. Entered Randolph-Macon College for Women, Virginia.
1914	Received Bachelor of Arts degree. Won two literary prizes.
1917	Married John Lossing Buck, May 13. Lived in North China.
1921	First daughter born. Taught English literature at University of Nanking.
1925	Returned to America. Attended Cornell University.
1926	Received Master's degree. Won Laura Messenger competition for "China and the West."
1927	Narrowly escaped death in army attack on Nanking.
1930	Published EAST WIND, WEST WIND.
1931	Published THE GOOD EARTH.
1932	Awarded Pulitzer Prize for THE GOOD EARTH.

1935	Divorced husband. Established home in Perkasie, Pennsylvania. Married Richard J. Walsh. Awarded William Dean Howells medal for fiction.
1936	Elected to National Institute of Arts and Letters.
1936-7	Adopted four Asian-American children.
1938	Received Nobel Prize for Literature.
1941-6	Published ASIA MAGAZINE with her husband.
1949	Founded Welcome House as an adoption agency.
1964	Founded Pearl S. Buck Foundation for homeless children in Asia. Continued writing.

Set in Weiss Roman, designed by Emil Rudolf Weiss
for the Bauer Typographic Foundry. Typography by
Joseph Thuringer and set at the Rochester Typographic
Service. Printed on Hallmark Eggshell Book paper.
Designed by Marjorie Merena.